CHILDREN'S ACTIVITY BIBLE

1st edition, 7th print
Copyright 2014 © Scandinavia Publishing House
Drejervej 15 3rd floor, DK 2400 Copenhagen NV, Denmark
Email: info@sph.as
www.sph.as

Text copyright © Leyah Jensen and Isabelle Gao
Illustrations copyright © José Pérez Montero

Activities and layout by Isabelle Gao
Graphic design: Gao Hanyu
Editor: Anne Clark
Puzzle checker: Linda Vium

Hardcover   ISBN 9788771321081
Softcover   ISBN 9788771321104
Printed in China

CHILDREN'S ACTIVITY BIBLE

Stories retold by Leyah Jensen and Isabelle Gao

Illustrated by José Pérez Montero

 SCANDINAVIA

Contents

THE NEW TESTAMENT

THE OLD TESTAMENT

The Very Beginning

Genesis 1:1-19

In the beginning, there was nothing but darkness.

There was no water and no land, no animals and no people. But in the silence, there was God. God had a plan. "Let there be light!" He said.

God divided the light from the darkness. He called the light day, and the darkness night.

Then God stretched space deep and wide. He placed the planets and the stars in the sky.

Circle the Earth that is different from the other ones.

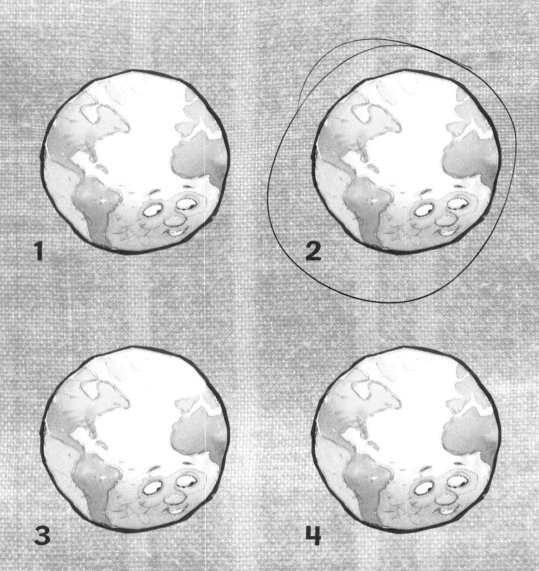

1

2

3

4

WORD SEARCH

Find the words in the crossword puzzle.

EARTH

MOON

A	E	X	I	L	S
D	A	R	K	T	U
P	R	M	O	O	N
S	T	A	R	G	W
Q	H	B	J	U	C
L	I	G	H	T	F

DARK

STAR

LIGHT

SUN

11

God Fills The Earth

Genesis 1:20-25

He created water and land on earth and put plants to grow. God filled the oceans with fish of amazing shapes and colors. God made birds to fly. Then He made animals of every kind to live on land. Some creatures were large and some were small. Some

were spiky, and some were soft.
God created all of them, big and small, and to each He gave His blessing.

SPOT THE DIFFERENCES

Can you find the 7 differences between these 2 pictures?

ADD UP

Add up the penguins and write down the number for each line.

+ =

+ =

+ =

+ =

Adam and Eve
Genesis 1-3

God had one last creation—people!

God made a man and named him Adam. Then, He made a woman and named her Eve. Adam and Eve loved each other very much. God told Adam and Eve to take good care of the animals. Then they all lived together peacefully in the beautiful garden called Eden. They could eat any fruit they wanted…except the fruit from one tree. But one day, an evil snake tricked them into eating it anyway. When God learned that they had disobeyed, He was very, very sad. He sent them away from the garden to never come back.

COMPLETE THE PICTURE

Find out where the missing pieces belong and draw a line to their correct places.

1

2

3

4

5

DOT-TO-DOT

Connect the dots to see which fruit Adam and Eve ate from the tree. Then color it.

Adam and Eve made a home for themselves outside of the garden. Soon Eve gave birth to a baby and named him Cain. Then they had another baby boy and named him Abel.

Cain and Abel each had a special job. Abel took care of the animals, while Cain took care of the fields. Cain gave God some of the crops from his harvest. But Abel gave God his best lamb. When God saw the gifts, He was happier with Abel's gift than Cain's. This made Cain very jealous of his brother.
Cain told Abel to come out into the field with him. Then, Cain attacked his brother and killed him! God was so angry that He sent Cain away from home, telling him that he would never be able to grow anything again.

Even after the terrible thing Cain had done, God kept him from harm and gave him a family of his own.

FIND THE PAIR

Find the 2 pictures of Abel that are exactly the same.

MATCH THE PARTS

Draw a line to match the two parts of the same animal.

Noah Builds an Ark

Genesis 6:5-22

Noah was a good man. He loved God. But the rest of the world had stopped listening to God. People were violent and sinful. So God told Noah, "I'm going to send a flood to destroy the world, but I have a special job for you."

God told Noah to build a boat. "Make it big," God said. The boat should also have many floors with many rooms and a big door in the side. After months of hard work, the boat was finished. God told Noah, "Gather up a male and a female of each kind of animal."

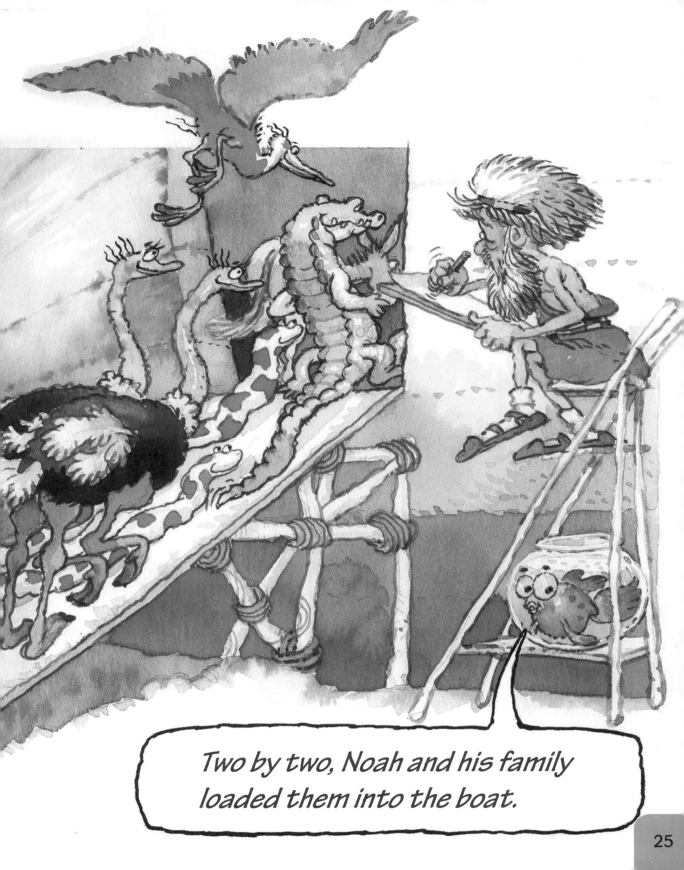

Two by two, Noah and his family loaded them into the boat.

COLOR THE ANIMALS

Use your colored pencils to complete the picture.

FIND THE ARK

Help the ostriches find the boat.

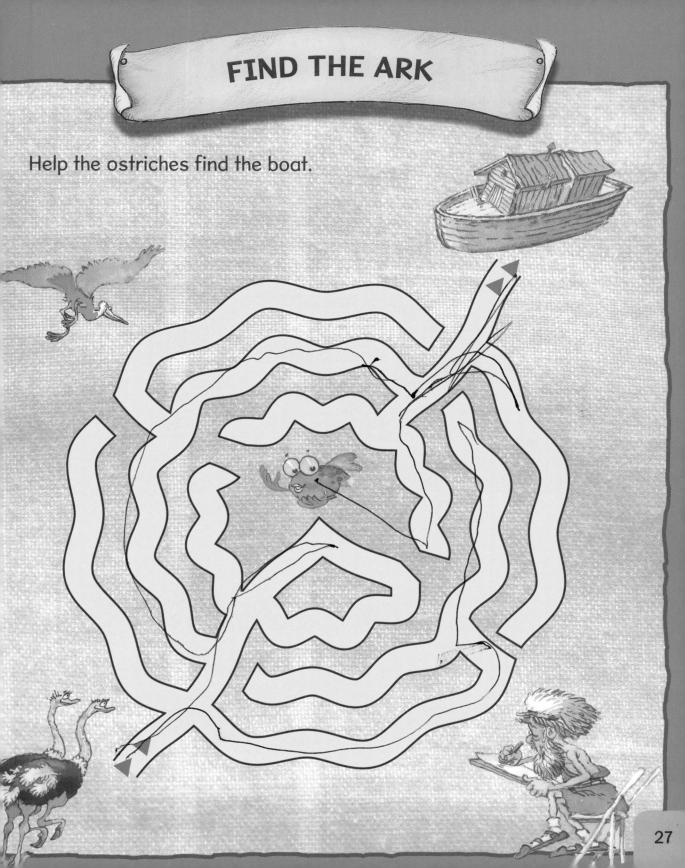

The Great Flood

Genesis 7:17-24; 8:1-19

Noah and his family went into the boat last and closed the door.
Then the rain began to fall. Soon the whole world was flooded with
water. Noah's boat floated safely on top of the waves.
After forty days and nights, the rain finally stopped.

Noah sent out a dove in search of land. The dove flew back to the boat with an olive branch in its beak!
God told Noah, "The flood is over." So Noah opened the great big door, and all the animals came out onto dry land.

FIND THE DIFFERENT DOVE

Which dove is different from the other ones?

DIFFERENT SIZES

Which bird is the biggest? Which one is the smallest?

God's Gift
Genesis 9:1-16

Noah and his family were grateful. Everyone praised God. Then Noah built an altar where he gave God gifts to thank Him for keeping them safe.

Then God made three promises to Noah. The first promise was that there would always be seasons...summer, autumn, winter, and spring.

God also said that there would always be night and day. His last promise was that He would never again flood the whole earth. To make sure that people never forgot this promise...

...*God placed a beautiful rainbow in the sky!*

33

COLOR BY NUMBERS

Color the rainbow by following the numbers.

1
2
3
4
5
6
7

1 Red	2 Orange	3 Yellow
4 Green	5 Blue	6 Purple
7 Violet		

Trace over the names of the colors.

RED

ORANGE

YELLOW

GREEN

BLUE

PURPLE

VIOLET

The Tower of Babel

Genesis 10:32-11:4, Genesis 11:5-9

Soon the world was filled with people again. Some of them settled in a place called Babel. The people in Babel decided to build a tower so high that it would reach heaven. "We will be famous, and God will be pleased with us!" they said to

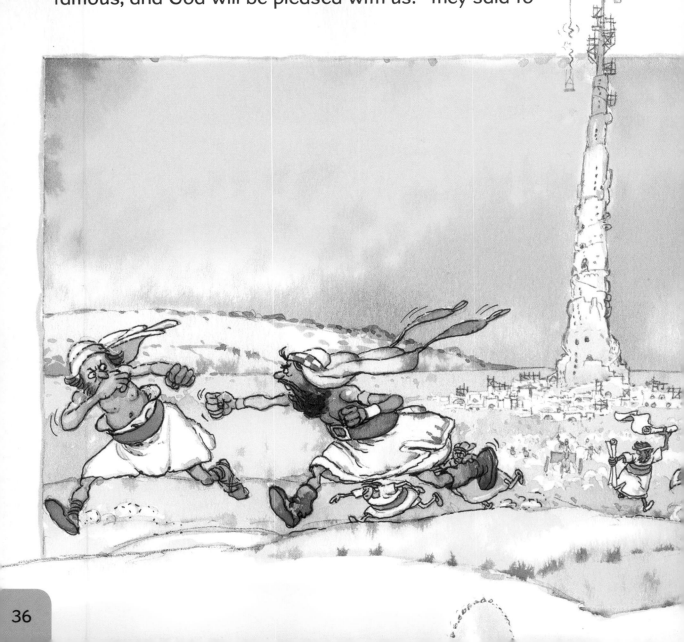

one another.

But when God saw the tall tower, He was not pleased. He saw that the people of Babel were no longer humble servants.

Instead, they were proud — believing they could reach God with their high tower. He punished the people by giving them each their own language.

No one could understand each other anymore! The tower could no longer be finished. They were too busy arguing in all their different languages.

SPOT THE DIFFERENCES

Can you find the 7 differences between these 2 pictures?

FIND THE PAIR

Find the 2 pictures that are exactly the same.

Abraham Follows God

Genesis 12-13, 17

Abraham was a special servant of God. God told him, "Take everything you own, and go to the land I will show you." Abraham did as God told him. He packed his camels and left with his wife Sarah.

They traveled through the desert and stopped to camp. God said, "Abraham, look up at the sky! Can you count the stars? That's how many children I will give you."

Abraham always remembered to stop and thank God for loving them so much.

COUNT THE ANIMALS

How many of each animal can you find in the picture?

dogs

camels

donkeys

DOT-TO-DOT

Connect the dots to see what God is showing to Abraham.

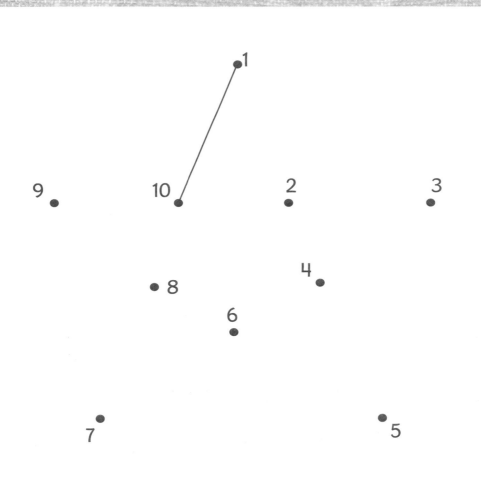

Abraham's Great Big Family

Genesis 13, 15, 17-18, 21

When Abraham and Sarah started getting old, they still had no children. But through all their journeys, they believed that God would give them the big family He had promised.

One day three travelers came by Abraham's camp. One of them was God. He promised Abraham a son. But Sarah laughed and thought, "I'm too old to give birth." The visitor said, "Why did Sarah laugh? Nothing is impossible for God."

Soon, Sarah had a baby boy. They named him Isaac. Sarah was very happy, and praised God for His wonderful gift.

Abraham and Sarah's family was very blessed because they followed God wherever He led them!

Can you find the 7 differences between these 2 pictures?

Joseph and the Colorful Coat
Genesis 37

Isaac had a son named Jacob, and Jacob had twelve sons. His favorite was Joseph.

One day Jacob gave him a beautiful coat. When Joseph's brothers saw that their father loved Joseph more than them, they became jealous.

One night, Joseph dreamt that he was ruler. When he told his brothers about the dream, they laughed, "Do you really think you will rule over us?" Now they hated Joseph more than ever.

The brothers made a plan to get rid of Joseph. They took his special robe and they threw him into an empty well.

When a caravan passed, they decided to sell him to the traders. Joseph was sold, and the caravan took him away to Egypt.

GO TO EGYPT

Which road leads the caravan to Egypt?

WORD SEARCH

Find the words in the crossword puzzle.

EGYPT

WELL

F	C	I	W	K	N
J	O	S	E	P	H
A	A	Q	L	U	V
C	T	X	L	O	Y
O	D	R	E	A	M
B	E	G	Y	P	T

ACOB

JOSEPH

COAT

DREAM

Joseph Forgives His Brothers

Genesis 39-46

Joseph became a slave in Egypt. But God was with him. Joseph worked very hard. His master liked him very much, but his master's wife told a lie that caused Joseph to be thrown in jail! There, with God's help, Joseph interpreted the prisoners' dreams and told them what they meant.

Two years later, Pharaoh, the king of Egypt, had a dream. Joseph told Pharaoh that the dream meant there was a famine ahead. Pharaoh was so thankful that he put Joseph in charge of storing food. The famine finally came. Back in Canaan, Joseph's brothers were hungry. They went to Egypt to buy food. They came before Joseph to ask for food, but they didn't recognized him. Joseph recognized them at once. Finally Joseph said, "I am Joseph! Don't be angry with yourselves for selling me as a slave. It was part of God's plan so that our family would not starve when the famine came!" His brothers were overjoyed! Joseph had forgiven them for the cruel things they had done to him. Joseph's family moved to Egypt, and they all lived happily together.

SPOT THE DIFFERENCES

Can you find the 7 differences between these 2 pictures?

FIND THE PAIR

Find the 2 pictures of Joseph that are exactly the same.

Baby Moses

Exodus 2:1-10

Long after Joseph died, a bad pharaoh ruled Egypt. He didn't like that there were so many Israelites in Egypt, so he forced them to become slaves. Then he ordered his soldiers to kill the Israelite babies.

One Israelite woman put her baby in a basket and sent him floating down the river. She hoped God would save him.

The princess of Egypt went down to the river. When she saw the basket, she took the baby out of the river and named him Moses.

He became her son. Moses grew up in the Pharaoh's palace just like a real prince.

FIND THE BASKET

Help the princess find baby Moses.

FIND THE RIGHT SHADOW

Draw a line to connect each picture to its shadow.

Moses Hears the Call of God

Exodus 1-4

Yet Moses knew that he was an Israelite. It made him sad to see how the Egyptians mistreated his people. One day he saw an Egyptian hitting an Israelite. When no one was looking… Moses killed the Egyptian. Pharaoh came after him, so Moses ran away. Moses settled in a new land although God had not forgotten His plan for him. While Moses was tending his sheep, God spoke to him from a burning bush! God's voice said, "Moses, I have chosen you to lead my people out of Egypt."

Moses wasn't so sure.

FOLLOW THE LETTERS

Follow each letter and write it down in the square at the bottom.
You will discover a word from the story.

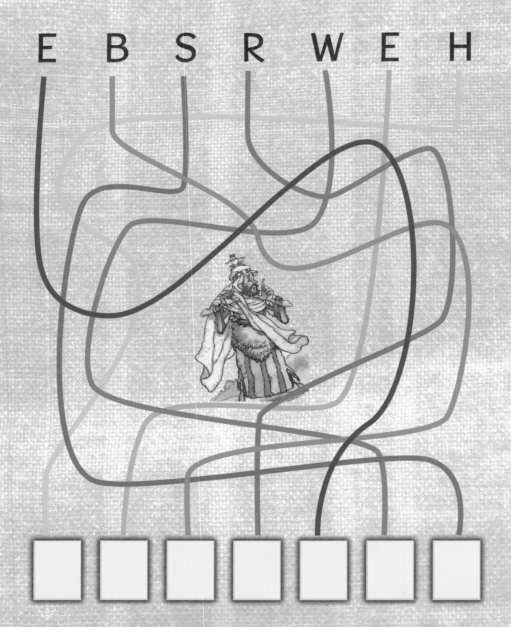

E   B   S   R   W   E   H

PUZZLE GAME

Find out where the missing pieces belong and draw a line to their correct places.

A

B

C

D

Moses Leads God's People

Exodus 5-16, 19-20, 33-34; Numbers 13-14; Deuteronomy 1

Moses obeyed God and went to the king of Egypt. "Let my people go!" he said. But the king was very stubborn. He told Moses, "No, your people cannot go." God punished the Egyptians for this. He sent ten plagues to destroy Egypt. First, He made their water go bad. Then, He sent insects, sickness, and storms! When many Egyptians died, Pharaoh at last changed his mind. He told Moses. "Get out of here, and don't ever come back!"

The king chased Moses and the Hebrew people to the edge of the Red Sea. God told Moses to lift his hands, and the sea opened up! The people crossed safely to the other side. When Pharaoh's army tried to follow them, God closed the waters again.

Moses and all of God's people were safe.

God gave Moses the power to do miracles. He also led Moses to the edge of the promised land. "This land flows with milk and honey," God said. "And it belongs to my people."

REACH THE RED SEA

Find the road that Moses and the Hebrew people took to reach the Red Sea.

SPOT THE DIFFERENCES

Can you find 7 differences between these 2 pictures?

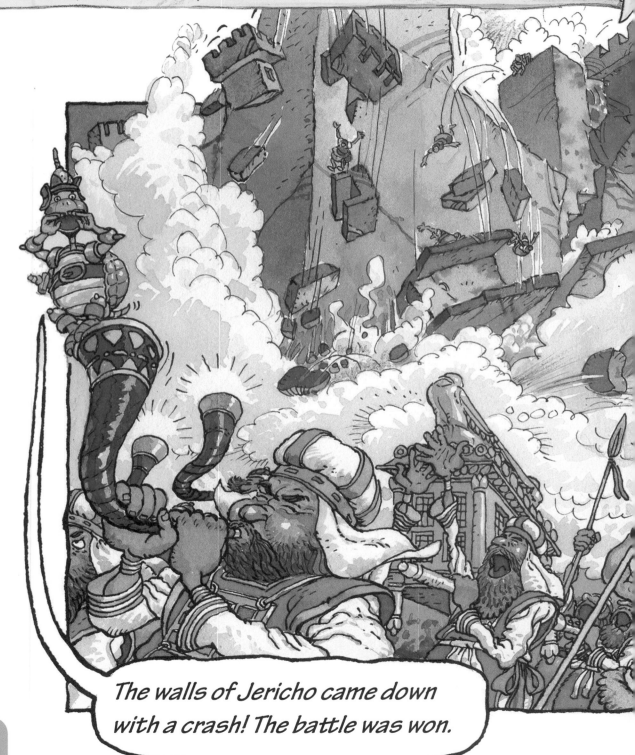

The walls of Jericho came down with a crash! The battle was won.

Joshua was Moses' helper. Joshua loved God with all his heart. When Moses died, God told Joshua, "Be brave, I will be with you wherever you go."

The first city Joshua had to go to was Jericho. The people there were trembling with fear and shut all the gates to the city. No one could go in or out. Yet God had a plan. He told Joshua, "March around the city of Jericho once every day. On the seventh day, shout praises and blow your horns. Jericho will be yours!"

Joshua did just as God told him. The priests went first carrying trumpets. Then came the army and the rest of the Israelites. One, two, three, four, five, six! On the seventh day, they blasted their horns, and the ground began to shake.

Count how many objects are in each box and write down the number in the circle.

ADD UP

Add up the objects and write down the number for each line.

Gideon and the Fleece
Judges 6

The people of Israel were in trouble. The cruel Midianites ruled over their land and took their food and animals. So they had to hide in caves.

One day a young man named Gideon saw an angel sitting under a tree. "God wants you to save Israel," the angel said. "Me?" Gideon could not believe it. God had promised to be with Gideon. Yet Gideon still wasn't sure that he would be able to beat the Midianites. The enemy was getting closer. Gideon rounded up a huge army. But God told Gideon to bring only a very small army of three hundred soldiers to fight the Midianites. Gideon gave each soldier a torch for one hand and a trumpet for the other.

Then they marched towards the Midianites. At the edge of the camp, the Israelites blew their horns. Then they gave a great shout. In the valley below, the Midianites became terrified and ran.

FIND THE RIGHT SHADOW

Draw a line to connect each picture to its shadow.

WORD SEARCH

Find the words in the crossword puzzle.

CAMP

ENEMY

B	D	C	A	M	P
T	S	E	R	I	U
O	K	N	M	F	H
R	G	E	Y	V	O
C	A	M	E	L	R
H	X	Y	J	Q	N

HORN

TORCH

CAMEL

ARMY

75

Samson the Super Strong

Judges 13-14, 16

When Samson was born, God blessed him and made him very strong. Someday, Samson was going to save his people from their ennemies. As a sign of his special purpose, God told Samson's parents that they should never cut his hair.

Samson became stronger and stronger the longer his hair grew. When his enemies came to arrest him, they tied him with rope. Then suddenly, Samson broke the ropes off!

He was a mighty warrior. The Israelites made Samson ruler.

DOT-TO-DOT

One day, an animal attacked Samson, but Samson was very strong and threw him off. Connect the dots to see what animal it was.

Ruth's Loyalty

Ruth 2-4

There was a woman named Naomi. She had two sons. One of them was married to a woman named Ruth.

Naomi's husband died, and her sons died too. So Naomi told Ruth to go home. But Ruth said, "I won't leave you. Where you go I will go. Your people will be my people, and your God will be my God."

Ruth and Naomi traveled to Bethlehem. It was a long journey.

Naomi and Ruth needed food, so Ruth went to the fields and picked up the leftover grain from a field belonging to a man named Boaz.

Naomi hoped Boaz would help Ruth find a new husband. Soon, Boaz and Ruth were married!

God blessed Ruth for her loyalty, and she became the great-grandmother of King David!

FIND RUTH'S HUSBAND

Help Naomi find Boaz.

HIDDEN WHEAT GRASSES

Find 7 hidden wheat grasses in the picture.

God Chooses David

1 Samuel 16

David was a shepherd who loved God with all his heart.
One day God told His prophet Samuel to go to Jesse's home. One
of his sons was going to be the new king. Samuel looked at each
of Jesse's big strong sons. "Do you have any other sons?" Samuel
asked. "Only David, the smallest," Jesse answered. "He is taking
care of the sheep." Samuel had him brought in. When Samuel saw
David, God showed him that this was the one. Samuel poured oil on

David's head. From that day on, David was powerful in all he did.

FIND THE PAIR

Find the 2 pictures of David and Samuel that are exactly the same.

COLOR BY NUMBERS

Color the picture below using the color code, and you will see what Samuel used to show that David was the chosen king.

1 Yellow   2 Blue   3 Orange   4 Brown

David Fights Goliath

1 Samuel 17

At this time, the Philistines were attacking Israel. They had a hero named Goliath. He was a giant. Goliath said, "Send someone to fight me!" David's brothers and the other soldiers were too afraid. But David said, "I will fight Goliath!" He collected five stones and put them in his bag. Then David went right up to Goliath.

"You come with a sword, but I come in the name of the Lord!" he shouted. David pulled out a stone and swung his slingshot. The stone hit Goliath right in the head!

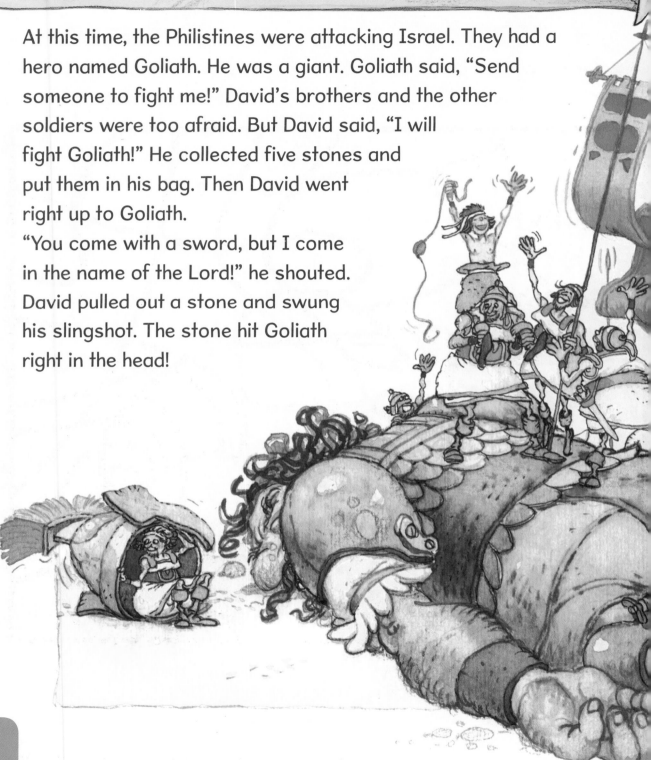

The giant fell facedown onto the ground. David was a hero! He became the next king of Israel.

Connect the dots to see what Goliath was holding to fight David.

FIND THE STONES

Help David find the stones to fight Goliath.

The Wisdom of King Solomon

2 Samuel 12; 1 Kings 3; 2 Chronicles 1

After King David died, his son Solomon
ruled Israel. God came to him in a dream.
Solomon said, "Lord, make me wise so
that I will know right from wrong."
God made Solomon the wisest king
that ever lived. One time two women
came to him. They were fighting over
a baby. "He's my son!" shouted one
woman. "No! He's mine!" said the
other. It seemed impossible to
know who the real mother was,
but wise Solomon had a plan to
find out.
"Cut the baby in half," he said.
The mother of the child cried,
"Give her the baby, but don't hurt
him!" Now Solomon knew who had
told the truth.
The people of Israel heard the story,
and realized how bright Solomon was.

SPOT THE DIFFERENCES

Find the 7 differences between these 2 pictures.

FIND THE PAIR

Find the 2 pictures that are exactly the same.

Elijah the Prophet

1 Kings 16-17, 19; 2 Kings 2

Elijah was God's special prophet. He
told Elijah, "I am going to send a
famine. No rain will fall for a long
time."

God promised to take care of
Elijah. He told Elijah to hide out
in the wilderness. God sent
ravens with food for Elijah to
eat. After a while, God spoke
to Elijah again and told him
to go to see a poor woman
and her son. He asked her
for bread, but she had only a
tiny bit of flour and oil. Elijah
promised that if she fed him,
she and her son would have
plenty to eat.

God rewarded her, her flour
and oil never ran out!

Who brought Elijah bread and meat to eat during the drought?

FIND THE POOR WOMAN

Help Elijah find the road to go to see the poor woman.

FIND THE DIFFERENT ONE

On each line, find the picture that is different.

The king was looking for a wife. He gathered the most beautiful women from all around. Esther was one of them. Everyone liked

Esther because she was so beautiful and good. When the king met her, he chose her as his wife.

Esther's cousin came to visit her. He would not bow to anybody but the Lord, and this made Haman, the king's official, furious. "We must kill the Jews!" Haman decided. So the king sent out an order for all the Jews to be put to death. Esther felt sad and worried. She had not told the king that she was a Jew too. Esther prayed, "Lord, what should I do?" She asked. God gave Esther courage. "Please save the Jews," she pleaded to the king. "They are my people!" The king listened to Esther and changed his order.

All over the kingdom, the Jewish people celebrated with joy.

ONE SINGLE ONE

Cross all the objects that you find more than once in the grid, and circle the last one that is left.

Daniel and the Lions

2 Kings 25; 2 Chronicles 36; Jeremiah 39-40, 52; Daniel 1

There was a terrible war in Israel. The King of Babylon attacked Jerusalem and took many Israelites back to his own land.

One of the prisoners was a boy named Daniel. Daniel was the king's favorite servant. He was wise and loyal and the King made him an important leader. The other leaders were jealous. They wanted to get rid of Daniel. So they planned a trick. They got the king to order everyone to bow to him. But Daniel would only bow to God. "Throw him in the lions' den!" said his enemies.

"My God has saved me!" Daniel cried.

Though the king loved Daniel, he was forced to punish him. And so, Daniel was thrown down into the den of lions. In the darkness Daniel prayed to the Lord. God sent angels to shut the lions' mouths. The next morning, the king rushed to the den to see what had happened. Daniel was safe.

FIND THE RIGHT SHADOW

Which shadow belongs to Daniel? Circle it.

Count how many of the following animals you find in the picture, and write it down in the boxes.

lions

bats

mice

Jonah and the Big Fish

Jonah 1-4

In a town called Nineveh, the people were doing bad things. God chose Jonah to go to the town and tell them to stop sinning. Jonah didn't want to go because the people there were his enemies. Instead he thought he could run away by getting on a boat that was going in the opposite direction to Spain.

God sent a storm. The sailors trembled. Jonah told them, "It's my fault. I thought I could run away from God. Throw me overboard!" The sailors threw Jonah over, and the storm stopped. God sent a giant fish to swallow Jonah up! Jonah prayed and prayed. He told

God how sorry he was for trying to run away. Jonah had finally learned his lesson. So at last, God told the fish to spit Jonah onto a beach. God said again, "Go to Nineveh!" This time Jonah obeyed. He told the people to turn their hearts to God, and they listened.

FIND THE ODD ONE

Find which fish or seashell is not in the picture with Jonah.

MATCH THE PAIRS

Draw a line to connect the two parts of the same animal.

THE NEW TESTAMENT

Mary and Joseph

Luke 1; Matthew 1

Mary was a young girl who lived in Nazareth. She had a pure heart, and she loved God. Mary was engaged to a carpenter named Joseph. God sent an angel to Mary. "I am Gabriel," the angel said. "I've come with good news! You will give birth to God's only Son." Mary answered the angel, "I am the Lord's servant. May His will be done."

The ruler gave an order that everyone had to get registered. So Joseph and Mary went on a long journey to Bethlehem, where Joseph was from. Mary rode on the back of a donkey.

When they finally got to Bethlehem, there was no room for them. Finally, they found a stable...

PUZZLE GAME

Find out where the missing pieces belong and draw a line to their correct places.

A

B

C

D

COLOR MARY AND JOSEPH

Jesus is Born

Matthew 1-2; Luke 2

Mary and Joseph stayed in a stable full of animals. It was time for Jesus to be born! Mary wrapped Him lovingly in clothes and laid him in a manger.

The angels in heaven rejoiced. God's Son had arrived!
Nearby, shepherds were watching their sheep. An angel appeared
to them, saying, "I bring you tidings of great joy—Christ is born!"
They hurried to see Jesus.

WORD SEARCH

Find the words in the crossword puzzle.

J	E	S	U	S	P
C	D	A	I	H	T
O	M	Q	X	E	B
W	A	N	G	E	L
F	R	U	A	P	K
V	Y	B	A	B	Y

ANGEL

COW

MARY

BABY

JESUS

SHEEP

COUNT THE ANIMALS

Count how many animals are in each box and write down the number in the circle.

What did the Magi follow to find Jesus?

The Wise Men

Matthew 2:7-12

Far away, three wise men also learned about Jesus. God put a special star in the sky to lead them to where Jesus was. After

many months, they arrived.
They brought expensive gifts of gold, frankincense, and myrrh.
Then they worshiped Jesus. They knew He was God's own son
because God had told them.

SPOT THE DIFFERENCES

Can you find the 7 differences between these 2 pictures?

LOOK FOR BABY JESUS

Draw over the line that goes from the Wise Men to baby Jesus.

Jesus Chooses His Disciples

Matthew 4:18–26:75

Jesus grew up.
One day, he saw two brothers named Simon and Andrew throwing their nets into the sea.
Jesus told the fishermen, "Let down your nets." They obeyed. When they pulled the nets in again, they were full of fish! The fishermen were amazed.
Jesus said to them, "Follow Me. I will make you fishers of men." Simon and Andrew left their nets and followed Jesus. As they walked along the sea, Jesus called to James and John who were in a boat. They also followed Jesus. Jesus chose twelve men in all.

FIND THE DIFFERENT ONE

Find the picture of Jesus and Simon that is different from the others.

PUZZLE GAME

Find out where the missing pieces belong and draw a line to their correct places.

A

B

C

D

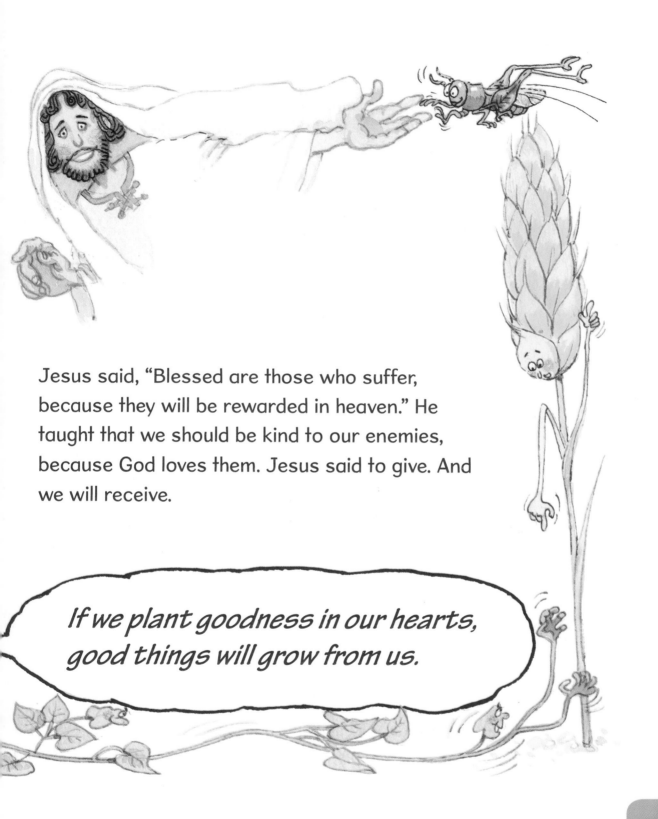

Jesus said, "Blessed are those who suffer, because they will be rewarded in heaven." He taught that we should be kind to our enemies, because God loves them. Jesus said to give. And we will receive.

If we plant goodness in our hearts, good things will grow from us.

SMALLEST AND BIGGEST

Find the smallest and the biggest grasshopper.

COUNT THE ANIMALS

Count how many objects are in each box and write down the number in the circle.

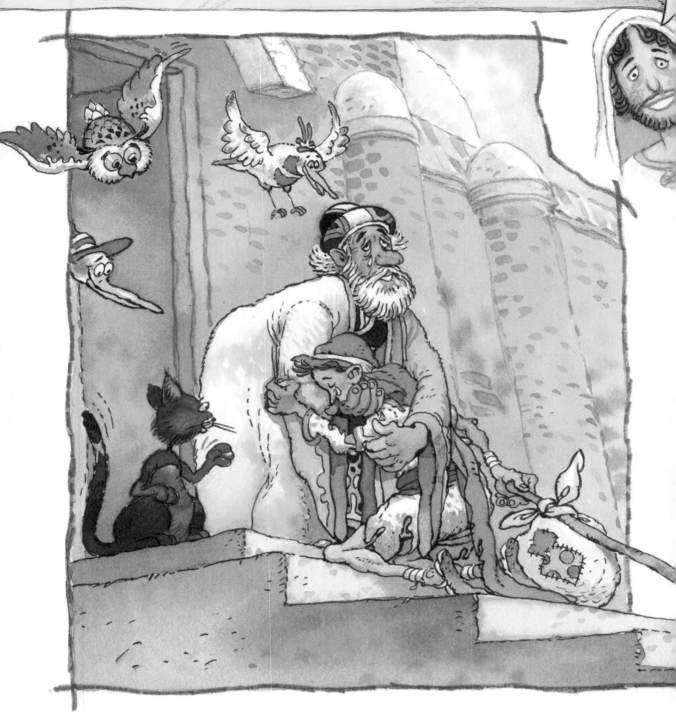

Jesus told this story: Once there was a man who had two sons. One day, the younger son told his father he wanted to leave home. He also asked his father to give him a lot of money.

The son traveled to a land far away. There he spent all his father's money with bad friends. Then he was left all alone with no money to buy food. So he got a job taking care of pigs. He was so hungry he even ate the pigs' food.

Finally, he decided to go back to his father and ask for forgiveness. The father was waiting at home.

As soon as he saw his son coming, he ran out and hugged him. "I forgive you, Son," he said. The father still loved his son no matter what he had done.

GO BACK HOME

Which road did the son take to go back to his father to ask for forgiveness? Find the right way.

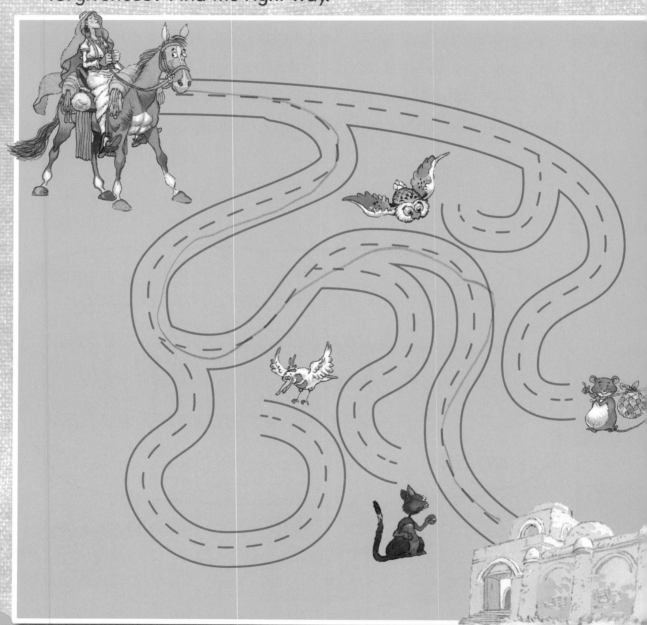

WORD SEARCH

Find the words in the crossword puzzle.

Z	H	A	Q	H	F
B	E	J	C	U	A
S	F	B	A	G	T
M	O	N	E	Y	H
R	H	O	R	S	E
T	D	S	O	N	R

MONEY

FATHER

SON

HUG

BAG

HORSE

Jesus Turns Water Into Wine

John 2:1-11

Jesus went to a wedding in Galilee with his disciples. His mother Mary was also there. Later on in the evening, the wine ran out. So Mary asked Jesus to help.

All the jars were empty, so Jesus told the servants to fill them with water. Then Jesus turned water into wine! The disciples smiled at one another. They knew that Jesus had done a miracle.

This miracle of Jesus turning the water into wine was Jesus' first miracle.

ONE SINGLE ONE

Cross all the objects that you find more than once in the grid, and circle the last one left.

FIND OBJECTS

Find the following objects in the picture.

Jesus Heals People

Matthew 9; Mark 2; Luke 5, John 11

People with all kinds of sicknesses came to Jesus, and He healed them.

One day, Jesus was teaching in a house. There was a crippled man outside who wanted to see Jesus, but the house was full. So the man's friends cut a hole in the roof and lowered him down.

Jesus saw that the man and his friends had faith. He said to the crippled man, "Get up!" The man obeyed. He could walk!

SPOT THE DIFFERENCES

Can you find 7 differences between these 2 pictures?

Can you find who is not in the house with Jesus?

1 2 3

4 5

145

Jesus Calms The Storm

Mark 4:35-41

One day, Jesus and His disciples were crossing a lake. Jesus fell asleep. Suddenly, a storm started. The boat began to fill with water. The disciples woke Jesus up crying, "We are going to drown!" Jesus commanded the storm to stop. All was calm. Then He said to His disciples, "Where is your faith?" The disciples were amazed—the wind and waves obeyed Jesus!

FIND THE RIGHT SHADOW

Find which shadow belongs to Jesus.

COUNT THE FISH

Write down the number of each type of fish you find in the picture.

flying fish

1

seahorses

2

schooling bannerfish

3

Jesus Feeds People

Mark 6:39-44, John 6:10-14

Jesus was teaching a huge crowd when it began to get late.
The disciples were worried. Where could they find food for
so many people? There was nothing for them to eat.

A boy gave Jesus two fish and five loaves of bread. Jesus
blessed the food. Then He began to break it...and filled
basket after basket!

All five thousand people ate until they were full. There was
even leftovers.

FIND THE ANIMALS

Can you find the animals in the picture?

Look at each picture and word, and copy the names under each picture.

FISH

_ _ _ _

BREAD

_ _ _ _ _ _

BASKET

B r E a d

Jesus Brings Lazarus to Life
John 11:1-44

Lazarus was a good friend of Jesus. One day, he got very sick. Jesus was away at that time and waited a few days before He went to see him in Bethany. When He arrived, Lazarus was already dead. Jesus went to the tomb and prayed. Then He shouted, "Lazarus, come out!" And Lazarus came back to life and came out!

Lazarus had two sisters. Do you know what were their names?

FOLLOW THE LETTERS

Follow each letter and write it down in the square at the bottom.
You will discover a word from the story.

A E Y B H N T

B E T H A N Y

Jesus Walks on Water

Mark 6:45-50; Matthew 14:28-36

One day, Jesus sent His disciples ahead in a boat while He went to pray. Soon a storm grew, tossing the boat. The disciples looked up, and they saw Jesus walking on the water towards them! At first He looked like a ghost.

"Don't worry, Peter," Jesus said. "It's me." But Peter wasn't sure. "If it's really you, then let me come out to you," he said.

"Come," Jesus replied. Peter stepped out of the boat. He began to walk on water too! Then he realized how strong the wind was and became afraid. Peter began to sink and cried, "Save me!"

So Jesus reached out his hand and pulled Peter up. "Where is your faith?" Jesus asked. After that, the disciples knew Jesus was the Son of God.

DRAW A BOAT

The disciples got into a boat to start their journey on the sea. Can you try to draw the boat?

Find the words in the crossword puzzle.

J	N	Q	S	P	A
E	W	A	T	E	R
S	A	I	O	T	Y
U	L	N	R	E	L
S	K	U	M	R	K
V	B	O	A	T	Y

BOAT

PETER

JESUS

STORM

WATER

WALK

Jesus and the Children

Mark 10:13-16

The children wanted to see Jesus too.
The disciples tried to send them away, but
Jesus said, "Let the little children come to
Me!" Then He blessed the children.
"You must each become like a child in
order to enter the kingdom of God," Jesus
told the disciples.

Jesus loved children very much. He said that they are special because they don't worry about being important.

How many men do you see in the picture below?

How many women do you see in the picture below?

How many children do you see in the picture below?

Connect the part of the clothing to whom it belongs.

Jesus in Jerusalem

Matthew 21:1-11

Jesus told His disciples that He must soon go to Jerusalem.

Jesus and His disciples came near Jerusalem. They found a donkey for Jesus. Large crowds had gathered to welcome Him, spreading clothes on the ground for Him to ride on. They waved branches and cried out, "Hosanna! Blessed is He!"

Finish drawing the palm leaf that people were waving to welcome Jesus.

How many branches can you find in the picture?

The Last Meal

Luke 22:7-23

It was time for the disciples to have the last supper with Jesus.
Jesus knew that he would soon return to His father in Heaven.
Jesus blessed the bread and wine and gave some to each disciple.
He told them to remember Him when they ate from now on.

Can you find these colors in the picture? Draw a line to connect the colors to the same color.

Blue

Pink

Purple

Red

Orange

FIND THE CUPS

 Find 7 cups in the picture.

Jesus is Arrested

John 18:2-8; Matthew 26:48-49

Jesus took His disciples to a garden. He was very sad and fell on the ground to God. "Your will be done," Jesus prayed.

Judas had brought the synagogue leaders and the soldiers to take Jesus away. "I must go," Jesus said. "This is God's plan."

The disciples became afraid and ran away. Jesus' enemies took Him to be judged.

FIND THE PAIR

Find the 2 pictures of Jesus and the soldier that are exactly the same.

Follow the dots to write the name of JESUS and then try to write it by yourself.

Peter Denies

John 18:12-14; Luke 22:54-62

When the people saw Peter, they said to him, "You were with Jesus!"

But Peter replied, "No I wasn't—I don't even know Him." Three times Peter lied about knowing Jesus. Then a rooster crowed. Peter realized that he had betrayed Jesus, and he wept. He was very sorry for what he had done.

Peter denied Jesus because he was afraid people would hurt him if they knew he was one of the disciples.

SPOT THE DIFFERENCES

Find the 7 differences between these 2 pictures.

Jesus on the Cross

Luke 23:32-44

The soldiers hurt Jesus then put Him on a cross.
Over Jesus' head, the soldiers hung a sign that said, "This is
Jesus, the King of the Jews." His enemies made fun of Him.
"If You are really the Son of God, then make a miracle by
getting down from the cross!" But Jesus knew it was the
will of God.

DRAW A CROSS

Draw on the dashes to make a cross!

COUNT

How many of these animals and objects can you find in the picture?

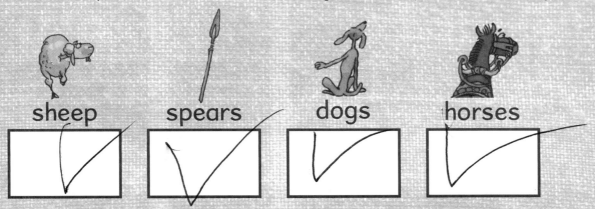

sheep ✓

spears ✓

dogs ✓

horses ✓

Jesus is Buried

John 19:31-34; Matthew 27:57-61

After Jesus had died, His friends took His body off the cross.
They wrapped Him in clean clothes.
Then they laid Him in a tomb of rock. Soldiers guarded the cave to make sure no one moved the rock.
Jesus' friends were very sad. Their beloved Jesus was gone.

Joseph of Arimathaea, a secret disciple of Jesus, asked if he could have Jesus' body to bury him. Do you know who he asked?

Can you find 7 differences between these 2 pictures?

COLOR BY NUMBERS

Color the picture below using the color code, and you will see what Jesus' friends used to see inside the cave.

1 Blue   2 Green   3 Yellow

Jesus is Alive

Matthew 28:1-10

After three days had passed, Jesus' friends went to see the tomb. Suddenly, there was a great earthquake! An angel from heaven moved the stone away from the tomb's opening.

Then he spoke to Jesus' friends. "Don't be afraid. I know you are looking for Jesus. He isn't here—He is risen! Come and see for yourselves".

They went into the tomb. Jesus was gone!

"Go and tell His disciples that Jesus is risen from the dead," the angel said. "You will see Jesus on the road."

Jesus' friends were so happy and ran to tell the disciples.

COUNT THE PEOPLE

How many women do you see in the picture?

How many soldiers can you find in the picture?

How many shoes do you see in the picture?

FIND THE PAIR

Find the 2 pictures of the soldier that are exactly the same.

Jesus Appears to the Disciples

John 20:19-23

One evening, the disciples were gathered together. They were hiding from those who wanted to hurt them for being friends with Jesus.

Suddenly, Jesus appeared! "Peace be with you," He said. The disciples were overjoyed to see Him. Jesus showed them His wounds. Then He gave them a special message—He was sending them into the world to do His work!

Can you guess whom they were hiding from?

HIDDEN BUTTERFLIES

 Can you find the 5 butterflies in this picture?

Jesus Goes to Heaven

Acts 1:3-11

It was time for Jesus to return to heaven, so He led the disciples out of the city. There He told them, "Go and teach people everywhere that Jesus came to forgive their sins."

Jesus gave the disciples the Holy Spirit. It would help them in the days to come.

Then He was taken to heaven. They were amazed. As He disappeared in a cloud, the disciples worshiped to God.

FIND THE ODD HAT

Find which hat goes with each person. One doesn't belong to anyone!

WHO IS LEFT?

Cross out all the people that appear twice in the grid. Who is left?

Saul is Blind

Acts 8:1-4; 9:1-18

After Jesus went to heaven, Christians were not treated well. One day a man named Saul was on his way to Damascus to look for believers. He was going to bring them back to Jerusalem as prisoners. Suddenly, a light from heaven flashed around him!

Saul fell to the ground. "Saul, why do you hurt Me?" he heard a voice say. "Who are you?" Saul asked. The voice answered, "I am Jesus. Now get up and go to the city." Saul was still blind when he arrived in Damascus. A man named Ananias took him by the hand. "Jesus has sent me to give you back your sight," he said. All at once Saul could see.

Help Saul go to Damascus.

205

Paul is Singing Praises

Acts 9:20-31; 16:16-40

Paul went to Jerusalem. He wanted to join the disciples, but they were afraid of him because of the bad things he had done before. Then Barnabas , one of the disciples, told the others how Saul had met the Lord and how he had preached in Damascus.

So they all became friends, and together they taught about Jesus. More and more people listened and believed.

Paul and his friends traveled far to spread the good news. One day, Paul and Silas were thrown in jail for preaching. They sang praises to God and the prison doors opened! The guard was afraid and asked, "What must I do to be saved?" Paul and Silas answered that he must believe in Jesus. The guard was grateful. Then Paul and Silas were released.

SPOT THE DIFFERENCES

Find 7 differences between these 2 pictures.

COLOR BY NUMBERS

Color the picture below using the color code, and you will see what the guard used to release Paul and Silas.

1 Orange   2 Green

Paul's Change of Heart

Acts 17-28

He traveled around the world and preached to people. "God loves you," he told them. "Believe in Jesus, and be one of God's children!" The more Paul preached, the more his enemies tried to hurt him. Paul was very brave by answering everyone who asked him questions. He was thrown in jail again and again.

In jail, Paul wrote about how to live by God's Word. He said that the Holy Spirit would teach us wisdom if we asked.

He wrote to churches and to friends and followers.

In one letter he wrote, "Nothing can ever separate us from God's love."

Connect the boats to their shadow.

ADD UP THE BOATS

Add up the boats and write down the number for each line.

God Promises a New World

Acts 5:12–5:24; 1, 2, 3 John, Jude, Revelation

John was one of the twelve disciples. He had watched Jesus perform miracles and listened closely to His teachings. When John was very old, he was given a special vision from God. God told Him that Jesus was going to come back to earth soon. Then John saw heaven. Believers from every nation were singing praises around the throne of God. John saw a new heaven and a new earth. God and His people were no longer separated.

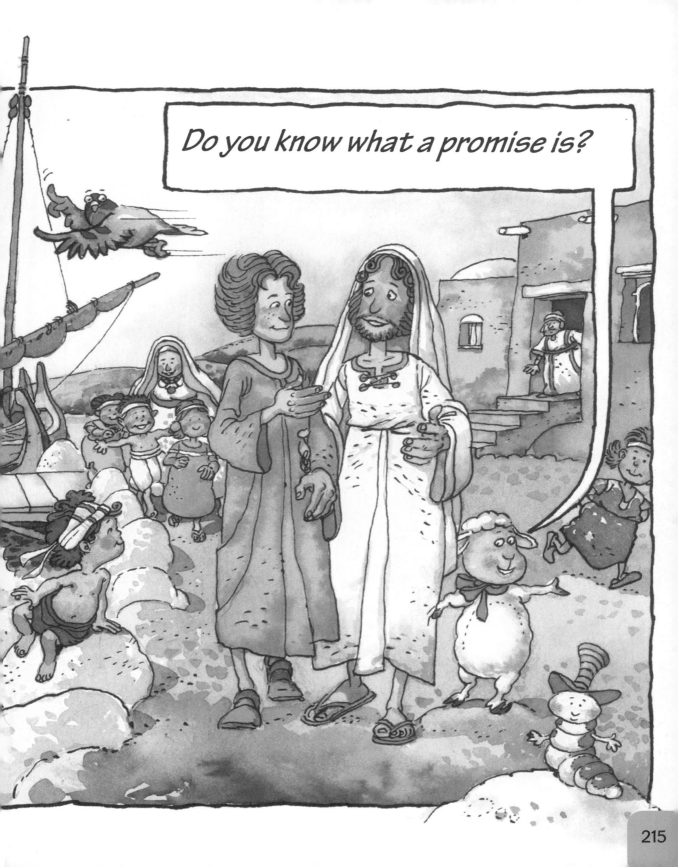

FIND THE DIFFERENT ONE

For each line, find which one is different.

1 2 3 4

1 2 3 4

COLOR BY NUMBERS

Color the picture below using the color code, and you will see what is watching Jesus and John as they talk.

1 Blue   2 Orange   3 Yellow

Jesus Will Come Back

1, 2, 3 John, Jude, Revelation

At the end of John's vision, Jesus spoke. "Listen, I am coming soon! I was in the beginning, and I will be there at the end."

In the beginning when God created the world, there was darkness. But when Jesus returns in the end, there will be light. Jesus is the light of the world.

If we let Him into our hearts, His light will shine through us. Someday we shall see Him in heaven, and there we will live in the joy of God's love forever.

God said, "I am making everything beautiful and new!"

WORD SEARCH

Find the words in the crossword puzzle.

OWL

BEE

TURTLE

ANT

FROG

WORM

B	F	A	N	T	A
D	R	A	T	U	W
J	O	W	L	R	O
M	G	N	R	T	R
O	K	U	M	L	M
U	R	B	E	E	Y

GAME SOLUTIONS

THE OLD TESTAMENT

(pages 10-11) The Very Beginning
Picture 3 is different from the rest.

A	E	X	I	L	S
D	A	R	K	T	U
P	R	M	O	O	N
S	T	A	R	G	W
Q	H	B	J	U	C
L	I	G	H	T	F

(pages 14-15) God Fills the Earth
Add-up: 2, 4 , 5 and 6 penguins

(pages 18-19) Adam and Eve

(pages 18-19) Adam and Eve (continued)
Dot-to-dot: an apple

(pages 22-23) Cain and Abel

(pages 26-27) Noah Builds an Ark

(pages 30-31) The Great Flood
Picture 2 is different from the rest.

biggest

smallest

(pages 38-39) The Tower of Babel

(pages 42-43) Abraham Follows God
Count the animals: 1 dog; 2 donkeys; 5 camels
Dot-to-dot: a star

(pages 46-47) Abraham's Great Big Family

(pages 50-51) Joseph and the Colorful Coat

F	C	I	W	K	N
J	O	S	E	P	H
A	A	Q	L	U	V
C	T	X	L	O	Y
O	D	R	E	A	M
B	E	G	Y	P	T

(pages 54-55) Joseph Forgives His Brothers

(pages 58-50) Baby Moses

Pages 62-63- Moses Hears the Call of God
The name is HEBREWS.

Pages 66-67 - Moses Leads God's People

(pages 70-71) General Joshua and the Promised Land

Count the objects: 5 helmets; 3 shields; 6 spears

Add-up: 4 shields; 5 helmets; 7 spears

(pages 74-75) Gideon and the Fleece

(pages 78-79) Samson the Super Strong
Dot-to-dot: a lion

(pages 82-82) Ruth's Loyalty

(pages 86-87) God Chooses David

Color by numbers: an oil jar

(pages 90-91) David Fights Goliath
Dot-to-dot: a sword

(pages 94-95) The Wisdom of King Solomon

(pages 98-99) Elijah the Prophet

Picture 3 of Elijah is different from the rest.
Picture 4 of the raven is different from the rest.
Picture 2 of the lizard is different from the rest.

(pages 102-103) Queen Esther
The single one is:

(pages 106-107) Daniel and the Lions
Shadow 3 belongs to Daniel.
Count the animals: 6 lions; 3 mice; 1 bat

(pages 110-111) Jonah and the Big Fish
This fish is not in the picture with Jonah:

THE NEW TESTAMENT

(pages 116-117) Mary and Joseph

(pages 120-121) Jesus is Born

J	E	S	U	S	P
C	D	A	I	H	T
O	M	Q	X	E	B
W	A	N	G	E	L
F	R	U	A	P	K
V	Y	B	A	B	Y

Count the animals: 5 owls; 3 sheep; 2 cows

(pages 124-125) The Wise Men

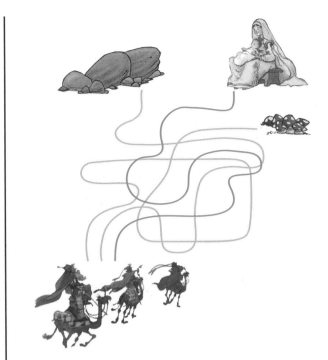

(pages 128-129) Jesus Chooses His Disciples
Picture 3 is different from the rest.

(pages 132-133) Jesus Tells About Kindness

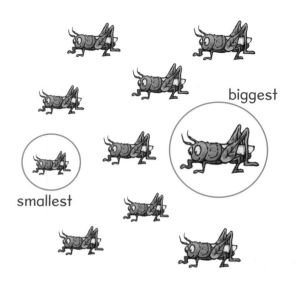

biggest

smallest

Count the animals: 2 mice; 4 field mice; 6 grasshoppers

(pages 136-137) The Loving Father

Z	H	A	Q	H	F
B	E	J	C	U	A
S	F	B	A	G	T
M	O	N	E	Y	H
R	H	O	R	S	E
T	D	S	O	N	R

(pages 140-141) Jesus Turns Water Into Wine

The single one is:

(pages 144-145) Jesus Heals People

Who is not in the picture: 5

(pages 148-149) Jesus Calms The Storm

Shadow 2 belongs to Jesus.

Count the fish: 4 flying fish; 3 seahorses; 3 schooling bannerfish

(pages 152-153) Jesus Feeds People

(pages 156-157) Jesus Brings Lazarus to Life
The name is: BETHANY.

(pages 160-161) Jesus Walks on Water

J	N	Q	S	P	A
E	W	A	T	E	R
S	A	I	O	T	Y
U	L	N	R	E	L
S	K	U	M	R	K
V	B	O	A	T	Y

(pages 164-165) Jesus and the Children
Count people: 5 men; 3 women; 6 children

(pages 168-169) Jesus in Jerusalem
Count the branches: there are 12 branches

(pages 172-173) The Last Meal

(pages 172-173) Jesus is Arrested

(pages 180–181) Peter Denies

(pages 184–185) Jesus on the Cross
Count: 5 sheep; 5 spears; 2 dogs; 3 horses

(pages 188–189) Jesus is Buried

Color by numbers: a lantern

(pages 192–193) Jesus is Alive
Count: 3 women; 2 soldiers; 9 shoes

(pages 196–197) Jesus Appears to the Disciples

(pages 200–201) Jesus Goes to Heaven
The odd hat is:

Who is left:

(pages 204–205) Saul is Blind

(pages 208-209) Paul is Singing Praises

Color by numbers: a key

(pages 212-213) Paul's Change of Heart
Add-up the boats: 3, 5, 6, 4 boats

(pages 216-217) God Promises a New World
Picture 2 of John is different from the rest.

Picture 4 of the boy is different from the rest.

Color by numbers: a crab

(pages 220-221) Jesus Will Come Back

B	F	A	N	T	A
D	R	A	T	U	W
J	O	W	L	R	O
M	G	N	R	T	R
O	K	U	M	L	M
U	R	B	E	E	Y